# Scholastic's
# The Magic School Bus
# Lost in the Solar System

*By Joanna Cole / Illustrated by Bruce Degen*

Touch icons within the book to
learn solar system facts!

Reveals theme
for Planet Bar

"You are Here"
for Planet Bar

Find Liz to hear a joke

Take the
Friz Quiz

*Special thanks to Chabot Space & Science Center*

It was trip day again in Ms. Frizzle's class. Everyone was excited. We were going to the **planetarium** to see a sky show about the **solar system**. Arnold's cousin Janet was visiting our class for the day.

Memory Trick

My Very Eager Mother Just Served Us Nine Pizzas

Sun  Mercury  Venus  Earth  Mars  Jupiter  Saturn  Uranus  Neptune  Pluto

SPACE RACE

WHAT IS THE SOLAR SYSTEM?
by John
The solar system is the **Sun** and all the bodies that orbit around it — the nine **planets**, their **moons**, the **asteroids** (chunks of rock) and comets (balls of ice and dust).

CLASS, AN ORBIT IS THE PATH OF A PLANET OR OTHER OBJECT AROUND THE SUN.

GO

STOP

As we were driving on the old school bus, Ms. Frizzle told us all about how the Earth spins like a top as it moves in its **orbit**. It was just a short drive to the planetarium, but Ms. Frizzle talked fast.

WHAT MAKES NIGHT AND DAY? by Phoebe

The spinning of the Earth makes night and day.

When one side of the Earth faces the Sun, it is daytime on that side. When that side turns away from the Sun, it is night.

SUN

EARTH

ROTATION

**Friz Quiz**

?

A  B  C

WHEN THE EARTH SPINS WE SAY IT ROTATES. THE EARTH MAKES ONE COMPLETE ROTATION — TURN — EVERY 24 HOURS.

repeat

3

When we got to the **planetarium** it was closed for repairs.
"Class, this means we'll have to return to school," said the Friz.
We were so disappointed!

On the way back, as we were waiting at a red light, something amazing happened. The bus started tilting back, and we heard the roar of rockets.

"Oh, dear," said Ms. Frizzle. "We seem to be blasting off!"

CHILDREN, WE ARE GOING THROUGH THE ATMOSPHERE —THE LAYERS OF AIR AROUND THE EARTH.

ROCKET SCIENCE

I GUESS WE'LL BE SEEING THE SOLAR SYSTEM AFTER ALL.

MY BUS HAS BIGGER ROCKETS THAN YOUR BUS.

YEAH RIGHT, JANET.

WHAT IS GRAVITY?
by Michael
Gravity is the force that pulls objects toward the center of the Earth.
    Other planets have gravity, too. Larger planets usually have more gravity. Smaller planets usually have less gravity.

FRIZ QUIZ ?

GRAND RE-OPENING!

FAMOUS ASTRONOMERS

Ptolemy 120 to 180

Nicholas Copernicus 1473 to 1543

Galileo Galilei 1564 to 1642

Johannes Kepler 1571 to 1630

Isaac Newton 1642 to 1727

BLAST FROM THE PAST

THE RAP

THE FACTS

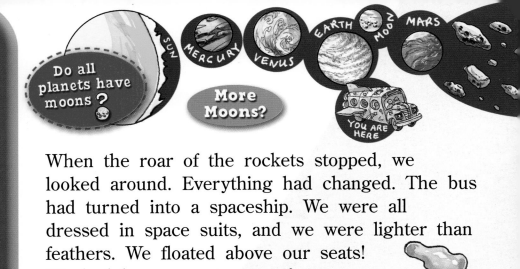

When the roar of the rockets stopped, we looked around. Everything had changed. The bus had turned into a spaceship. We were all dressed in space suits, and we were lighter than feathers. We floated above our seats!
We had become **astronauts!**

WHY DO PEOPLE FEEL WEIGHTLESS IN SPACE?
by Phil
A spaceship and the people in it both go into orbit around the nearest planet or sun. When this happens, the people are no longer pulled toward the floor of the ship, so they float around.

EXERCISE DAILY

The Friz said our first stop would be the Moon. We got off the bus and looked around. There was no air, no water, no sign of life. All we saw were dust and rock and lots and lots of **craters**. Ms. Frizzle said the craters were formed billions of years ago when the Moon was hit by **meteorites**.

We left the Moon and zoomed toward the Sun, the biggest, brightest, and hottest object in the solar system. Jets of super-hot gases shot out at us from the surface. Thank goodness Ms. Frizzle didn't get *too* close!

THE SUN IS A STAR
by Carmen
Our Sun is an average star like the ones we see in the night sky.

DID YOU KNOW?

HOW BIG IS THE SUN?
by Gregory
Our Sun measures more than **a million kilometers** across. More than one million Earths could fit inside it!

FRIZ QUIZ
?
T   F

Solar Flares

HOT!

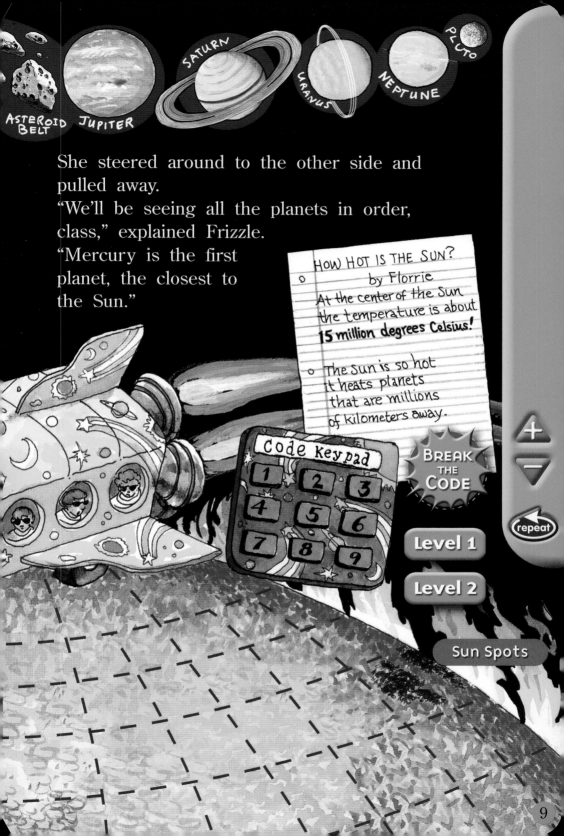

ASTEROID BELT  JUPITER  SATURN  URANUS  NEPTUNE  PLUTO

She steered around to the other side and pulled away.

"We'll be seeing all the planets in order, class," explained Frizzle.

"Mercury is the first planet, the closest to the Sun."

HOW HOT IS THE SUN?
by Florrie

At the center of the Sun the temperature is about **15 million degrees Celsius!**

The Sun is so hot it heats planets that are millions of kilometers away.

Code keypad

1 2 3
4 5 6
7 8 9

BREAK THE CODE

Level 1

Level 2

Sun Spots

repeat

9

How did the planets get their names?

YOU ARE HERE

SUN
MERCURY
VENUS
EARTH
MOON
MARS

Mercury was a dead, sun-baked planet. "This planet is a lot like our Moon. There is no water and hardly any air," said the Friz. "Notice the craters on its surface as we pass by."

THE SUN LOOKS TWICE AS BIG HERE AS IT DOES FROM EARTH.

THAT'S BECAUSE MERCURY IS SO CLOSE.

TOO CLOSE! LET'S GO!

GO

MUSICAL CRATERS

STOP

10

Before long, we felt ourselves being pulled in by the gravity of Venus—the second planet from the Sun. Venus was completely covered by a thick layer of yellowish clouds.

"We will now explore the surface of Venus," said Ms. Frizzle.

WE'RE GAINING WEIGHT, AND WE HAVEN'T EVEN HAD LUNCH.

WE WILL BE HEAVIER HERE THAN ON THE MOON OR MERCURY BECAUSE VENUS HAS MORE GRAVITY.

WHY ARE VENUS'S CLOUDS YELLOW?
by Tim
Earth's clouds are white because they are made of water vapor.
Venus's clouds are made mostly of a deadly yellow poison called sulfuric acid.

NAME THAT PLANET

Below the clouds, Venus was as dry as a desert. The ground was covered with rocks. And it was HOT! It was about **460 degrees Celsius**! That's *much* hotter than an oven baking cookies!

**TEMPERATURE QUEST**

500°C
450°C ← Venus (460°C)
400°C
350°C
300°C ← Cannon ball melting (327°C)
250°C
200°C ← Cookies baking (190°C)
150°C
100°C ← Water boiling (100°C)
50°C ← Body (37°C) temperature
0°C ← Water freezes (0°C)

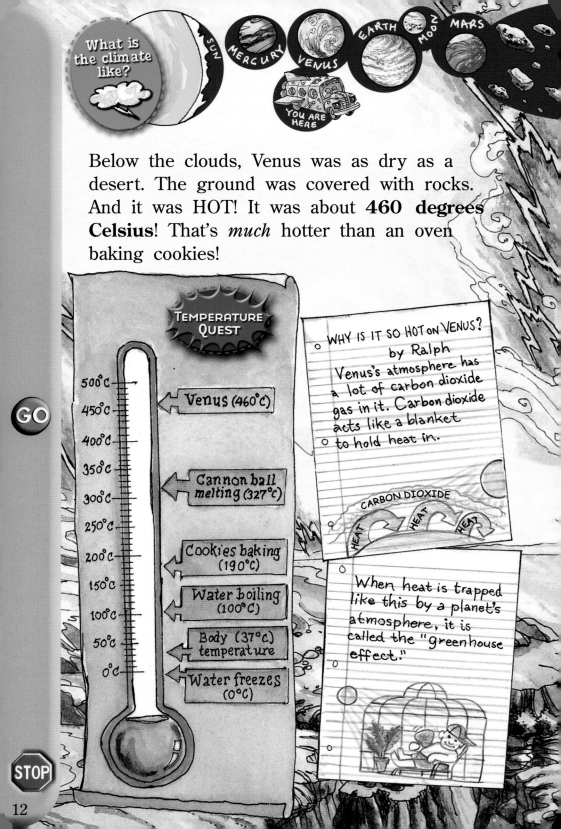

WHY IS IT SO HOT ON VENUS?
by Ralph

Venus's atmosphere has a lot of carbon dioxide gas in it. Carbon dioxide acts like a blanket to hold heat in.

CARBON DIOXIDE

HEAT  HEAT  HEAT

When heat is trapped like this by a planet's atmosphere, it is called the "greenhouse effect."

GO

STOP

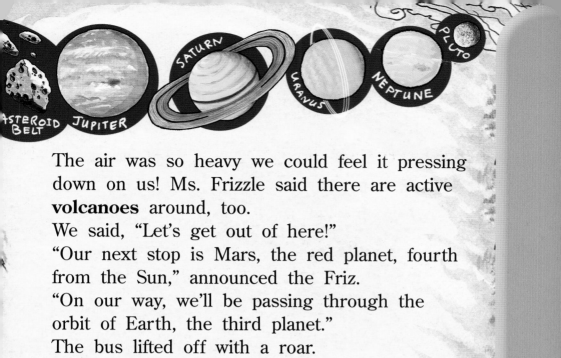

The air was so heavy we could feel it pressing down on us! Ms. Frizzle said there are active **volcanoes** around, too.

We said, "Let's get out of here!"

"Our next stop is Mars, the red planet, fourth from the Sun," announced the Friz.

"On our way, we'll be passing through the orbit of Earth, the third planet."

The bus lifted off with a roar.

THERE'S NO LIFE ON VENUS, CLASS.

I'VE BEEN TO MARS LOTS OF TIMES.

IT'S TOO HOT!

JUST IGNORE HER.

IT'S TOO DRY!

THERE'S TOO MUCH ACID!

LET'S LEAVE!

As we came close to Mars, we passed its two moons, which are called Phobos and Deimos. Compared to our Moon, they were tiny. And they weren't even round!

Why aren't Mars' moons round?

GO

Phobos
(18 miles long)

Deimos
(9 miles long)

Volcano

Soil

THOSE ARE MOONS?

THOSE MOONS LOOK LIKE POTATOES.

LONG AGO, THERE MAY HAVE BEEN WATER IN THOSE CHANNELS.

IN GREEK, PHOBOS MEANS FEAR AND DEIMOS MEANS PANIC.

STOP

Looking down, we saw a huge **canyon.** Ms. Frizzle said it was as long as the United States. There was a volcano three times taller than the tallest volcano on Earth. And all around, there were **channels** that looked like dried-up river beds.

Polar Ice Cap

Canyon

Channels

EARTH IS THE BEST PLANET FOR LIFE. THAT'S WHY I LIVE THERE.

JANET LIKES TO BE THE BEST.

WE NOTICED.

TRUTH SLEUTH

Fact    Fiction

"Mars is the last of what we call the **inner planets!**" Ms. Frizzle shouted above the roar of the rockets. "We will now be going through the **asteroid belt** to the **outer planets!**"

GO

ISN'T SPACE TRAVEL EXCITING, ARNOLD?

I REALLY PREFER VIDEOS.

EXIT

AIR LOCK KEEP THIS DOOR CLOSED

SOLAR SYSTEM SWEEP

Moon Mania

Far Out Facts

Grab Bag

SATURN

URANUS

NEPTUNE

PLUTO

ASTEROID BELT   JUPITER

YOU ARE HERE

Thousands of **asteroids** were spinning all around us. All at once, we heard the tinkling of broken glass. One of our tail lights had been hit by an asteroid.
Ms. Frizzle put the bus on **autopilot** and went out to take a look. She kept on talking about asteroids over the bus radio.

THE ASTEROID BELT
by Shirley
The area between the inner and the outer planets is called the asteroid belt. It is filled with thousands and thousands of asteroids.

THE LARGEST ASTEROID IS ONLY 1/3 THE SIZE OF OUR MOON. MOST ASTEROIDS ARE THE SIZE OF HOUSES OR SMALLER.

repeat

I WISH SHE'D COME INSIDE.

Suddenly there was a snap. Ms. Frizzle's tether line had broken! Without warning, the rockets fired up, and the bus zoomed away! The autopilot was malfunctioning.

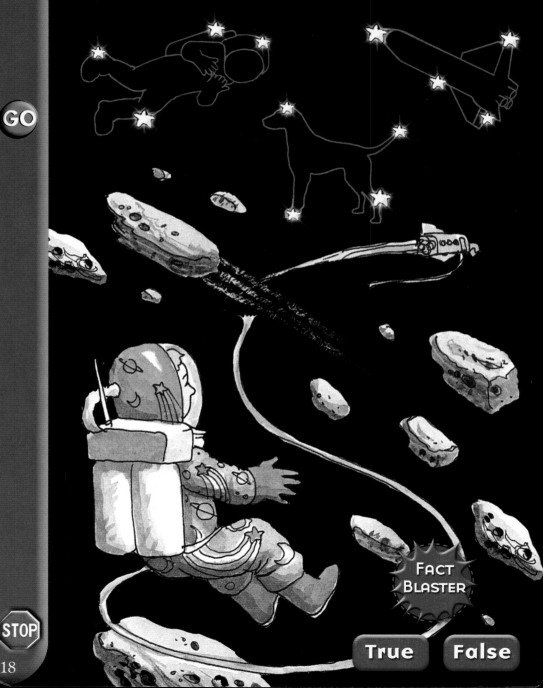

GO

FACT
BLASTER

STOP

True    False

On the radio, Ms. Frizzle's voice grew fainter and fainter. Then she was gone. We were on our own! We were lost in the solar system!

Most of us were too scared to move. But Janet started searching the bus. In the glove compartment she found Ms. Frizzle's lesson book. As she began reading from it, a huge planet came into view. "Class, this is Jupiter," Janet read.
"It's the first of the outer planets, and the largest planet in the solar system."

**IS THAT A FACT?**

**Fact** **Opinion**

"As we approach Jupiter, we can see some of its many moons."

"Arnold, are you listening?"

JANET SHOULDN'T TOUCH MS. FRIZZLE'S THINGS.

BOY, MS. FRIZZLE PLANS EVERYTHING!

BUT THIS IS AN EMERGENCY!

We thought the school bus was going to land. But there was no solid ground to land on. Jupiter is a "gas giant"—a planet made almost entirely of gas. As we left Jupiter, we wondered and worried. Would we ever get home?

Great Red Spot

repeat

"Jupiter is so big that more than one thousand Earths could fit inside it."

**YOUR WEIGHT AND FATE ON JUPITER**

| Earth Weight | Jupiter Weight |
| --- | --- |
| 85 lbs. | 215 lbs. |

MS. FRIZZLE, WHERE ARE YOU?

Don't worry, you'll lose those extra pounds, soon!

Which planets can you see from Earth?

SUN  MERCURY  VENUS  EARTH  MOON  MARS

The next sight made us forget our troubles. It was Saturn, a **gas planet** like Jupiter. It had swirling clouds and lots of moons. But the most incredible thing about Saturn was its rings. It was the most beautiful planet in the solar system!

Exploring Space

Naked Eye

Optical Telescope

Radio Telescope

ASTEROID BELT

JUPITER

SATURN

URANUS

NEPTUNE

PLUTO

YOU ARE HERE

THE FLOATING PLANET
by Phoebe
Saturn is made of materials that are lighter than water. If there were a bathtub big enough, Saturn could float in it!

IT'S A MYSTERY

Space Probe

Space Station

Hubble Space Telescope

repeat

Next was Uranus, a blue-green gas planet with faint gray rings and moons. Some scientists think they might be made of chunks of graphite—the material used in pencils on Earth.

THE TIPPED OVER PLANET
by Ralph
Uranus spins differently from the other planets.
It seems to be lying on its side compared to most other planets in the Solar system.

Uranus    Earth    Sun

"Methane gas in its atmosphere makes Uranus look blue."

YOU LOOK KIND OF BLUE YOURSELF.

I'M FREEZING!

THAT'S BECAUSE WE'RE SO FAR AWAY FROM THE SUN.

ASTEROID BELT  JUPITER  SATURN  URANUS  NEPTUNE  PLUTO  YOU ARE HERE

The bus was going faster and faster, and we couldn't control the autopilot. We swept past stormy Neptune, another blue-green planet—eighth from the Sun. All we could think about was finding Ms. Frizzle!

"Neptune is the last of the giant gas planets."

WE'RE ALMOST OUT OF GAS OURSELVES!

THE NEAREST SERVICE STATION IS 4,000 MILLION KILOMETERS AWAY.

repeat

FRIZ QUIZ
? A B C

HOW LONG IS A YEAR?
by Tim
A year is the time it takes for a planet to go all around the sun. Neptune and Uranus are so far away from the sun that they have very long years.

long orbit    short orbit

LET'S MAKE A YEAR

| PLANET | How Long One Year |
|---|---|
| Mercury | 88 Earth days |
| Venus | 225 Earth days |
| Earth | 365 Earth days |
| Mars | 687 Earth days |
| Jupiter | 12 Earth years |
| Saturn | $29\frac{1}{2}$ Earth years |
| Uranus | 84 Earth years |
| Neptune | 165 Earth years |
| Pluto | 249 Earth years |

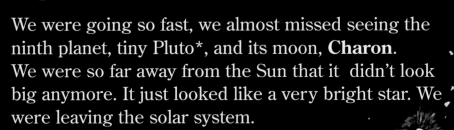

We were going so fast, we almost missed seeing the ninth planet, tiny Pluto*, and its moon, **Charon**. We were so far away from the Sun that it didn't look big anymore. It just looked like a very bright star. We were leaving the solar system.

*Every 248 years, Neptune's orbit is further out than Pluto's. Then Neptune is the ninth planet. But most of the time, Pluto is the ninth planet from the Sun.*

IS PLUTO A REAL PLANET?
by Wanda
Some scientists think Pluto was once a moon of Neptune. It may have escaped from the orbit around Neptune. Then it became a real planet in orbit around the Sun. Pluto was the last planet discovered in our Solar system.

BEYOND PLUTO:
STARS AND MORE STARS
by Alex
Beyond our solar system are billions and billions of stars. There are so many stars and they are so far away that our minds cannot even imagine it. Some of those stars have planets, and some of those

planets could have life on them, just like our earth.

Charon

Pluto

Janet flipped rapidly through Ms. Frizzle's book. Suddenly she found something new—the instructions for the autopilot. We punched in ASTEROID BELT on the control panel. Slowly the bus turned around. It was working! We were going back!

ASTEROID BELT **

Auto-Pilot

repeat

ZOOMTRON

EARTH

ZOOM OUT    ZOOM OUT    ZOOM OUT

ZOOM IN    ZOOM IN    ZOOM IN

PLANET    SOLAR SYSTEM    GALAXY    UNIVERSE

ZOOMTRON

When we reached the asteroid belt, there was Ms. Frizzle!

With Frizzle back at the wheel, the bus headed straight for Earth. We reentered the **atmosphere** and landed with a thump. Everything was back to normal.

BOYS AND GIRLS, WE ARE ARRIVING ON EARTH, THE THIRD PLANET FROM THE SUN.

THUMP

At last, it was time to go home. It had been a typical day in Ms. Frizzle's class. Now we had only one problem. Would anyone ever believe us when we told about our trip?

It Came From Outer Space